DUCKS
OFFICIAL
GUIDE

First published in Great Britain in 2013 by Hodder Children's Books

Written by Claire Sipi, with pages 74-77 and 84-87 by Sarah Courtauld.
Interior layout by ninataradesign.com

1

A Catalogue record for this book is available from the British Library.

ISBN: 978 1 444 91393 4

Printed in Spain

The paper and board used in this paperback by Hodder Children's Books are natural recyclable products made from wood grown in sustainable forests. The manufacturing processes conform to the environmental regulations of the country of origin.

Hodder Children's Books
A division of Hachette Children's Books
338 Euston Road, London NW1 3BH
An Hachette UK company
www.hachette.co.uk

CONTENTS

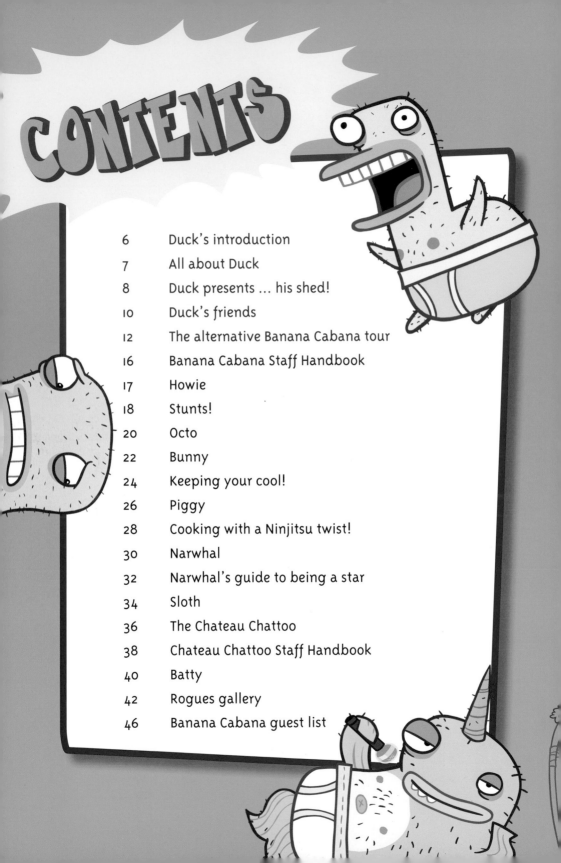

6   Duck's introduction

7   All about Duck

8   Duck presents ... his shed!

10   Duck's friends

12   The alternative Banana Cabana tour

16   Banana Cabana Staff Handbook

17   Howie

18   Stunts!

20   Octo

22   Bunny

24   Keeping your cool!

26   Piggy

28   Cooking with a Ninjitsu twist!

30   Narwhal

32   Narwhal's guide to being a star

34   Sloth

36   The Chateau Chattoo

38   Chateau Chattoo Staff Handbook

40   Batty

42   Rogues gallery

46   Banana Cabana guest list

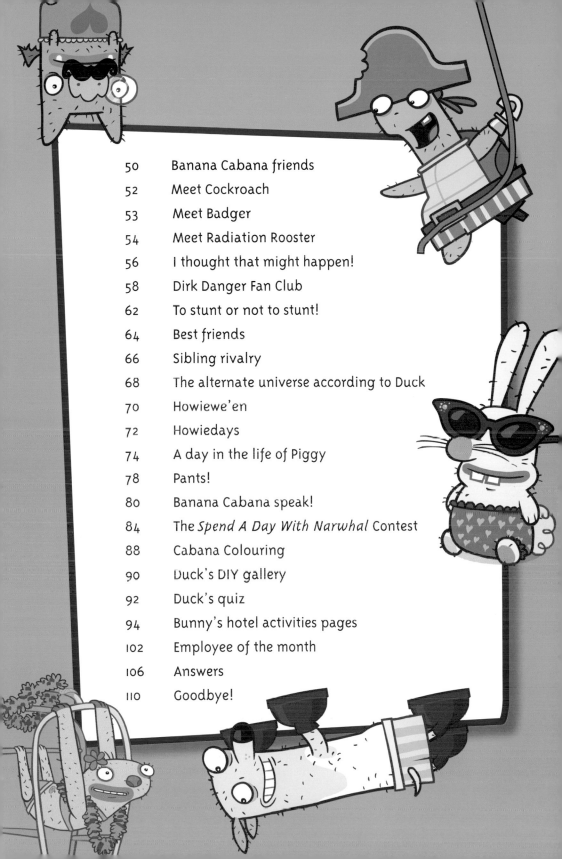

50   Banana Cabana friends

52   Meet Cockroach

53   Meet Badger

54   Meet Radiation Rooster

56   I thought that might happen!

58   Dirk Danger Fan Club

62   To stunt or not to stunt!

64   Best friends

66   Sibling rivalry

68   The alternate universe according to Duck

70   Howiewe'en

72   Howiedays

74   A day in the life of Piggy

78   Pants!

80   Banana Cabana speak!

84   The *Spend A Day With Narwhal* Contest

88   Cabana Colouring

90   Duck's DIY gallery

92   Duck's quiz

94   Bunny's hotel activities pages

102   Employee of the month

106   Answers

110   Goodbye!

Welcome, friends, fellow ducks and all other Almost Naked Animals fans!

I had a dream ... at least, I think it was a dream. I saw Howie, and he told me to write a book about the Banana Cabana. He also told me to put licorice in my navel and drink gravy. But I think I will start with the book.

If you find any stains, rips, or missing pages, it is probably because I am using some of these pages as napkins. Writing is hard work, and it makes me very hungry. Oh yes. I am eating some of the pages as well. Very tasty.

I hope that you enjoy the pages of this book that I have not eaten. If you need me, you can find me in my shed. I will be having a secret party. Please do not tell yourself that I said that, though.

With regards,

Archibald William Nightingale Duck III

Pssst! We just found out he's the King of Shedsylvania. No, really.

ALL ABOUT DUCK

(according to his friends)

STAFF PASS

Name: **DUCK**

Job: Banana Cabana's handy animal.

Likes: Funny stuff, sandcastles, lasers and alternate universes

Dislikes: Bread crumbs, cloudy days, itchy feet

Ahhh, Duck … you gotta love him, even if he is (how can we put this politely?) just a little bit weird! Duck is friend to everyone and everything. He's always got a solution to any problem you can throw at him. He may appear to be oblivious to the world around him, but occasionally, within his own quackers alternate universe, he has a moment of pure genius and his unusual and quirky talents save the day!

In Duck's unique world anything can happen … and it often does! He sleeps in the hotel storage cupboard and spends a lot of time in his shed … what he does there, we're not quite sure.

I did not write this.

7

MY PHOTO ALBUM

(Starring my shed!)

Duck-copter!

What do you call a D.I.Y. duck?
A duck-of-all-trades!

I took all of Piggy's spray-cheese
to my shed and ate it ...

Building the world's biggest can,
to test my new can-opener!

I am going to my shed. I can fix things. I have some of my best ideas in my shed. Come on, let me show you …

This is top secret. Please pretend you did not see this picture.

Eeeek! Where did this egg come from?

I am sure I can use this precious rock to make something useful.

I hate cloudy days.

Did you just try to make a joke?

MY FRIENDS

Howie is always happy to help out a friend in need!

Howie: employee of the month, every month!

Kitchen danger! Piggy no like his special sauce!

Who is that good-looking model?

It is fun making friends with hotel guests!

What could be better than spending time with friends?

Chicken pox alert!

Underpants alert!

I love a party in the bathroom.

alternative
THE ^ BANANA CABANA TOUR

Welcome! Stay at this great hotel — there are always empty rooms. I work here fixing things, so do not worry if everything in your room is broken, that is completely normal.

I am going to my shed to fix things in a moment, but I will show you around the Banana Cabana if you come now, because Howie, the manager, has told me to.

Do you like eating crayons? My favourite flavour is green.

Beachfront

There is a beach. With sand. If you go swimming you can find yourself a pet shark or crab. Do not worry if you hear screaming — apparently, some of our guests are not too fond of these pets.

Gazebo and pool area

If the sand and sea are not your thing, then you can use our pool. Sometimes we fill it with gravy!

Hello, Bunny!

Not now, Duck, can't you see I'm busy trying to get these lazy creatures to do some exercise!

Okie donkey!

Bunny is nice. She will make you exercise whether you want to or not.

Hot tub

Try out our relaxing hot tub. PARRRRRRP! Look at those pretty bubbles. Oh. I have not turned it on yet.

The Banana Cabana lounge

This hotel offers non-stop entertainment, night and day, and day and night, and daytime and night-time, and throughout the day and night, and … where am I? Oh, yes, pull up a booger chair and listen to that one-horned fish, Narwhal. He will be sure to sing you to sleep.

The Banana Cabana kitchen

The food at this hotel is like nothing you have tasted before.

Rooms

I do not know where you are going to sleep — I am sure Howie or Octo will find somewhere for you. I like to sleep in this lovely store cupboard. I have lots of fun in here.

… oh, you are still here! What was I saying?

Yes, this is a great place to stay if you want to have fun. I am going to my shed now. If you want to know who works here, have a look at this booklet. Enjoy!

BANANA CABANA STAFF HANDBOOK

Welcome to our semi-fine establishment. We hope you enjoy your stay. We knew our star rating at some point, but we seem to have misplaced our stars recently ... never mind that, we can guarantee that you will have a holiday here like you've never had before! Our staff are here to welcome you and make your stay as comfortable and enjoyable as possible. Please don't hesitate to ask any questions you may have ... if you can find us, we'll gladly help you. Otherwise, we'll be somewhere having fun!

Howie, and the rest of the Banana Cabana gang

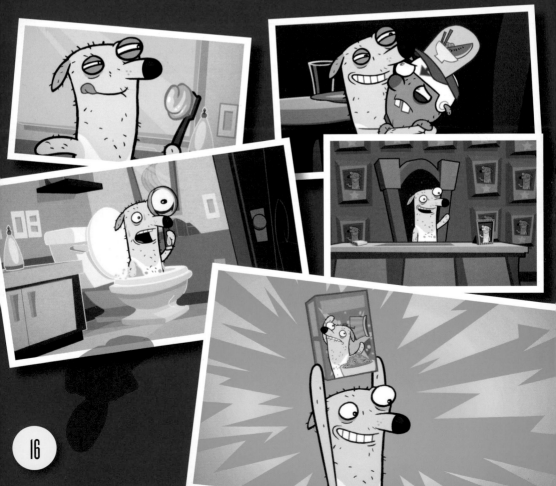

STAFF PASS

Name: **HOWIE**

Job: Manager of the Banana Cabana

Likes: Trampolines, running fast, ear wax

Dislikes: Silence, quitters, bubble baths

The fun-loving manager of this great hotel is always cheerful, a touch impulsive and loves a challenge. His style of management could certainly be described as unusual and high-energy. He doesn't believe in planning, preferring to 'go with the moment'. He's certainly spontaneous!

Howie has been a lifelong fan of Swedovlakian superstar stunt-animal extraordinaire, Dirk Danger, and it has always been his dream to become a world-famous stunt dog just like his hero. His best friend, Octo, sometimes wishes Howie's dream was something else. Something safer, like counting clouds.

Howie and Poodle's father gave them a hotel each to run as they wanted to.

STUNTS!

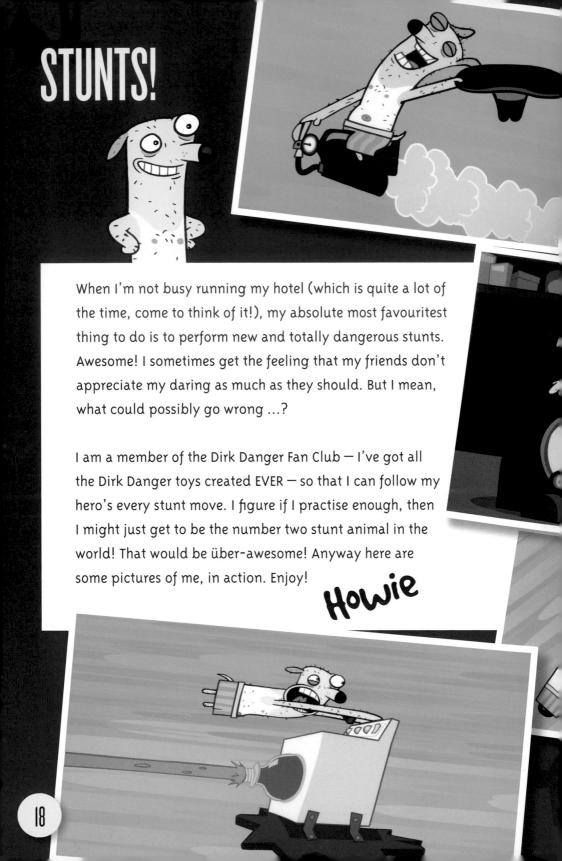

When I'm not busy running my hotel (which is quite a lot of the time, come to think of it!), my absolute most favouritest thing to do is to perform new and totally dangerous stunts. Awesome! I sometimes get the feeling that my friends don't appreciate my daring as much as they should. But I mean, what could possibly go wrong …?

I am a member of the Dirk Danger Fan Club — I've got all the Dirk Danger toys created EVER — so that I can follow my hero's every stunt move. I figure if I practise enough, then I might just get to be the number two stunt animal in the world! That would be über-awesome! Anyway here are some pictures of me, in action. Enjoy!

Howie

STAFF PASS

Name: OCTO

Job: Front desk clerk at the Banana Cabana

Likes: Firm mattresses, clean teeth, pop-up books

Dislikes: Slippery floors, most condiments, clowns

This slightly nervous eight-legged desk clerk is in the perfect job because he has an eye for detail and would have the hotel running smoothly and efficiently if only Howie would not drag him into so many dangerous situations and distract him from his desk duties.

His life-long ambition is to remove all possible causes of danger from any given situation. He is a quivering, jiggling, long-suffering and loyal best friend to Howie. So much so, that he breaks all his own health and safety rules, and goes against his better judgement, to support Howie in all his crazy plans … just because that's what BFFs do.

STAFF PASS

Name: BUNNY

Job: Activities Director (see pages 94–101 for Bunny's fun pack of poolside activities)

Likes: Princesses, stickers, rainbows

Dislikes: Slow days, broken mirrors, armpits

The Banana Cabana is lucky to have an Activities Director with so much energy and enthusiasm, and she is the perfect hostess — if everything is going well, Bunny is sweetness and light itself! Now, no one expects anybody to be happy all the time — everyone has their off days, after all — but, word of advice, if Bunny seems a little off-colour then it is probably best to keep out of her way. She's sure to be back to her sweet self sooner or later, and we can guarantee that she'll let you know where she is and what she is doing, with her usual efficiency.

23

KEEPING YOUR COOL ...

... when everyone around you is losing theirs, or getting in your way, or just not doing what you have told them to do!

What's the point of pretending to be nice, if you don't feel nice?

1. If a certain nervous desk clerk is taking their time to sort out your schedule, take a deep breath, count to five, walk away, don't shout, don't stamp your paws, and come back in half an hour.

2. If you have a tendency to be a bit tense and highly strung, do not, really DO NOT volunteer to wear the hotel mascot, KIKMEE. We cannot help you if you do, and wipe our hands of any responsibility for your actions.

3. Your friends don't mean to be afraid of you, so when they run for the hills, try not to take it personally, and challenge yourself to get through the rest of the day without snapping.

4. Always reward yourself with a little treat of your own choice if you get through a day (OK, let's make this a little easier — an hour) without shouting or wondering why you were put on this imperfect planet.

5. Try to 'turn your mad into glad' by throwing some cool moooves on the dance floor and shimmying away your anger! It works, really! And you will impress your friends at the same time.

6. Blow into a brown paper bag, a balloon or even an inflatable bouncy castle — you'll feel so dizzy you won't have time to be angry!

7. Take a moment to enjoy the little things in life (and try not to worry that one leg on your beach lounger is shorter than the other!).

8. If all else fails, put a blindfold on, stick a nose-plug in your nostrils, cover your ears with earmuffs and put on a pair of mittens. If you can't see, smell, hear or touch anything, then there'll be nothing to get mad at!

OK, so maybe I have teensy-weensy bit of a temper.

Got to stay calm. Got to stay calm.

Normally I'm as sweet as a peach!

STAFF PASS

Name: PIGGY

Job: Chef at the Banana Cabana Hotel

Likes: Ninjitsu, cheese, scooping things

Dislikes: Snow cones, greedy weasels, not scooping things

No one is quite sure where Piggy comes from, or what he did before he came to work at the Banana Cabana, but one thing is for sure — he certainly has the creative personality common to all master chefs: he is passionate, loud and takes his work very seriously.

His menus are quite diverse — no one really knows what the ingredients are, but we can guarantee that you will never have tasted anything like them before!

Piggy is even scarier than he might look — he is Ninjitsu trained. Keep on his good side if you want to avoid getting a karate chop or being scooped!

COOKING, NINJITSU STYLE

Piggy was taught by the greatest Ninjitsu Chef of all time … Master Ferret. Five years on, Piggy has still not graduated Ninjitsu Chef school because of the angry gumbo incident. Piggy longs to pass the final test and earn his puffy chef hat …

Piggy scared of Master!

Piggy will take his final test to become a Ninjitsu Chef!

Piggy ready for Gumbo Challenge.

Big danger spice CHILLANTRO!

Gumbo get hot. And angry. Piggy run from school never go back.

If Piggy fail again, no more puffy hat to cover funny-shaped head.

The Final Challenge!

Piggy passes the test! Piggy is worthy of puffy chef hat!

STAFF PASS

Name: NARWHAL
Job: Entertainer/performer
Likes: Butter, horn polish, magic and wonder
Dislikes: Green jellybeans, social studies, ring tosses

The only thing bigger than this hotel entertainer's horn is his ego! Our resident crooner, Narwhal, loves nothing more than performing to his adoring fans. He is one smooth, charming operator, wooing the crowds with his silky buttery voice. Between stage performances, Narwhal can be found staring at the love of his life in the mirror.

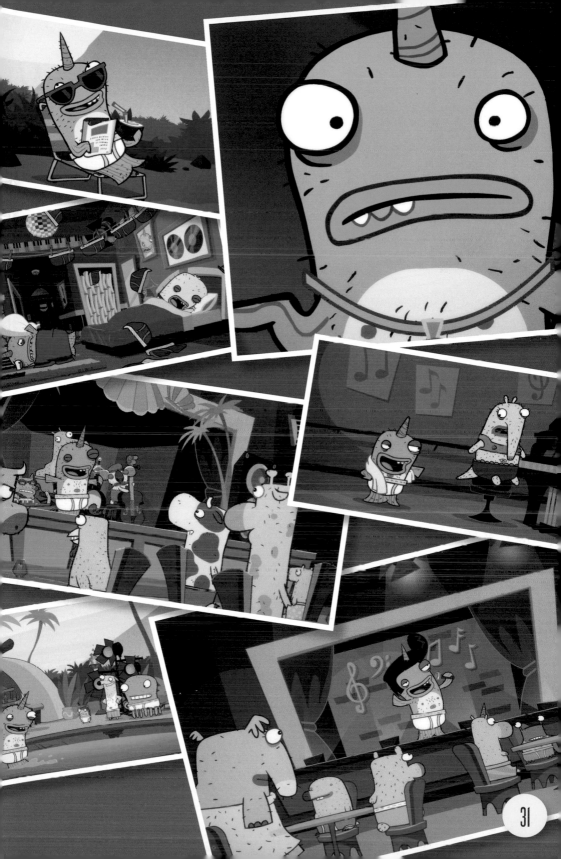

NARWHAL'S GUIDE TO BEING A STAR

Heeerrre's Narwhal! The one and only, fin-tastic, diddley-bop, buttery singing sensation!

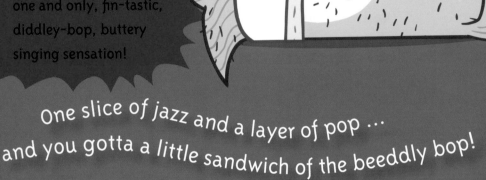

One slice of jazz and a layer of pop … and you gotta a little sandwich of the beeddly bop!

Howdy folks, I've gotta little down-time to slip you a few star tips on how to be the numero uno stage performer (well, make that numero two-o, baby, as there's only room at the top for one, and that's me!).

1. You've gotta keep yourself in top condition for those long hours performing to your adoring fans.
2. Believe in yourself, don't let anyone (yes, that means you Barney Beluga!) or anything get you down, look in the mirror and tell that handsome fella staring back at you that you were born to perform!
3. Get a look — wigs are cool, or try some sparkly shades, baby — just remember to keep it buttery and polished. Your fans do NOT want to see a shabby lounge legend up on that stage. Keep in the groove.

4. The voice — it's the tool of your trade — so be sure to keep it warmed up (think soft butter, and you'll be able to hit the right note) and smooooth! You'll have the crowds eating out of your fins with a few 'oooos' and 'la-la-la-las'!

5. You gotta chill before a show — after all, you owe it to your fans to look your best.

6. Vary your style — but remember, your fans will always flip out for a classic sweet love song (think of me and you'll know what to do, baby!).

7. And finally, sing every song like it's your last one — heart and soul mixed with a sensational dollop of bibbity-bop!

STAFF PASS

Name: SLOTH
Job: Bellhop
Likes: Lounging, HOWIE, makeovers
Dislikes: Long walks, line dancing, old cheese

Full of good intentions, our love-struck bellhop will do her best to get your luggage to your room, but you might need to go out and buy yourself some new stuff, as she probably won't get to your room before you need to check out!

The trouble is, not only is Sloth seriously S-L-O-W, but most of the time her heart isn't in her job because it's beating with love for Howie. Poor ol' soppy Sloth — she's smitten and swooning, but Howie is sadly oblivious to her adoring smiles and sighs!

Howie, you're so dreamy!

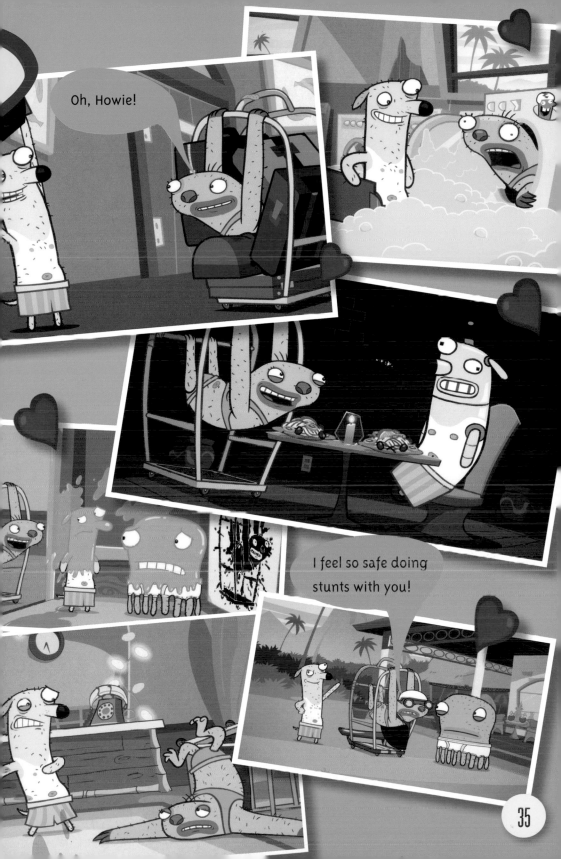

THE CHATEAU CHATTOO

Attention, all discerning holiday-makers! Once you have seen my magnificent hotel, you WILL NOT want to stay anywhere else, EVER!

The Chateau Chattoo is situated on its own island — away from the terrible riff-raff that you will find staying at that gross hotel across the bay. We are ultra-ritzy and cater only to the elite and upper classes. If 'fancy' and fountains are your thing, then call NOW to reserve a room for a holiday that you will never forget!

And don't forget to admire the glorious statues of me, dotted about our stylish resort — a remarkable likeness, don't you think?

CHATEAU CHATTOO STAFF HANDBOOK

STAFF PASS

Name: POODLE

Job: Hotel Manager of the Chateau Chattoo

Likes: Fountains, golden bricks, custard

Dislikes: Howie, Howie's friends, uncomfortable chairs

You can call her 'Princess Poodle' if you want because, let's face it, she thinks she's royalty already. She hardly has to lift a finger running her super-fine hotel resort, because her hench-animal Batty does all the hard work for her.

Poodle doesn't like to mention that she has a brother ... she doesn't know how she and Howie can be related. And she really doesn't understand how he manages to keep open his hotel across the bay. In her opinion, it shouldn't be allowed — and, in fact, she's working on a plan to shut the Banana Cabana down for good!

Batty, watch out, Poodle's on the warpath again!

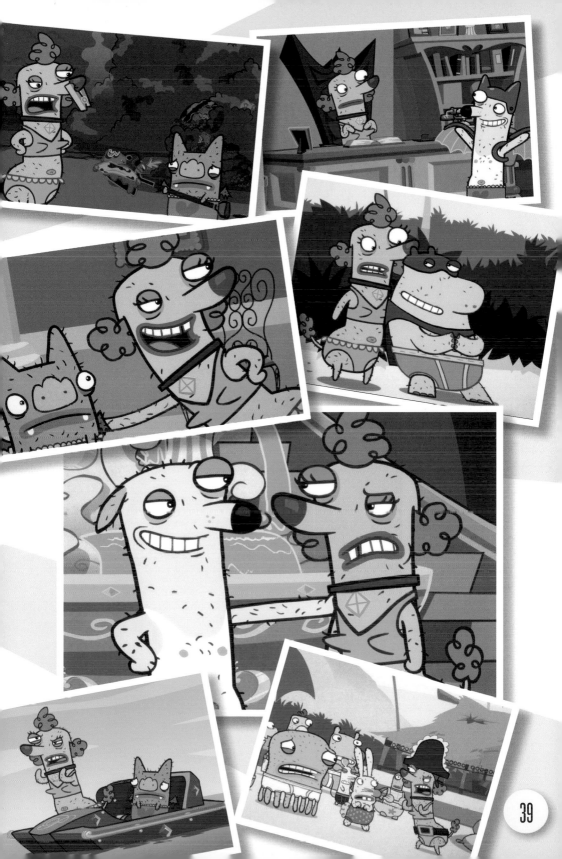

STAFF PASS

Name: BATTY

Job: Manager's assistant

Likes: Fidgeting, interpretive dance, fancy ice cream

Dislikes: Flying, weak handshakes, AM radio

You could not wish for a better assistant than Batty. He is loyal, even when he knows things will not end well for him ...

Batty spends all his time trying to please his boss, by attending to her every need and whim. He should get 11 out of 10 for effort, but sadly for him, Poodle never praises his efforts or gives Batty her approval.

Sorry, boss.

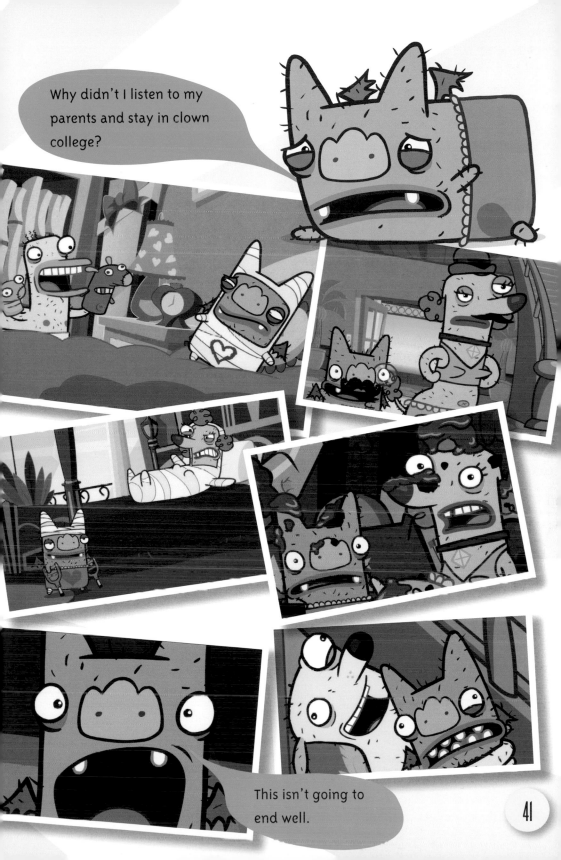

41

ROGUES GALLERY

Everybody (except Howie and Duck!) knows that Poodle would do anything to try and shut down the Banana Cabana ... and, believe it or not, there are other animals — and forces of nature — that don't appreciate Howie, his misfit crew and their antics at the hotel.

YETI This huge beast likes to cause mischief and will stop at nothing to win, whatever it takes. He's no fan of Howie and would happily help Poodle with her plans to take over the Banana Cabana. Don't mention watermelons in front of Yeti — he is obsessed with them and is one of the fiercest competitive watermelon eaters the island has ever seen.

Likes: Watermelons, unusual things and casual mischief

Dislikes: Working out, cold tea and close talkers

HiPPO

This big fella thinks he is some sort of superhero (probably because he spends too much time in a virtual world!), and regularly wears a cape and eye mask. He has even been known to carry a wooden simulation battle sword in public. Hippo is a video-game expert and loves playing with action figures (well, who doesn't?).

Likes: Action figures, capes, fierce competition

Dislikes: Cheap glue, silver medals, quicksand

MAYOR TROUT

The Mayor is loved by everybody, and he loves everybody back ... except for Howie! The trouble is that Howie causes a path of accidental destruction everywhere the Mayor goes. Mayor Trout is so fed up that he would happily see the Banana Cabana shut down, and frequently tries to find excuses to close the hotel's doors for ever!

Likes: Statues, important meetings, choo-choo trains

Dislikes: Howie ... yes, just Howie!

LARRY

Howie's pretend brother, Larry ...
... the actor that Poodle hires to try and trick Howie out of the Banana Cabana.

You can't quit, Larry ... we have a deal. Tough it out, it's only a matter of time until he gives you half the Banana Cabana!

Larry, my long-lost brother! I didn't know that I'd lost you, or that you existed ... you must've been really lost!

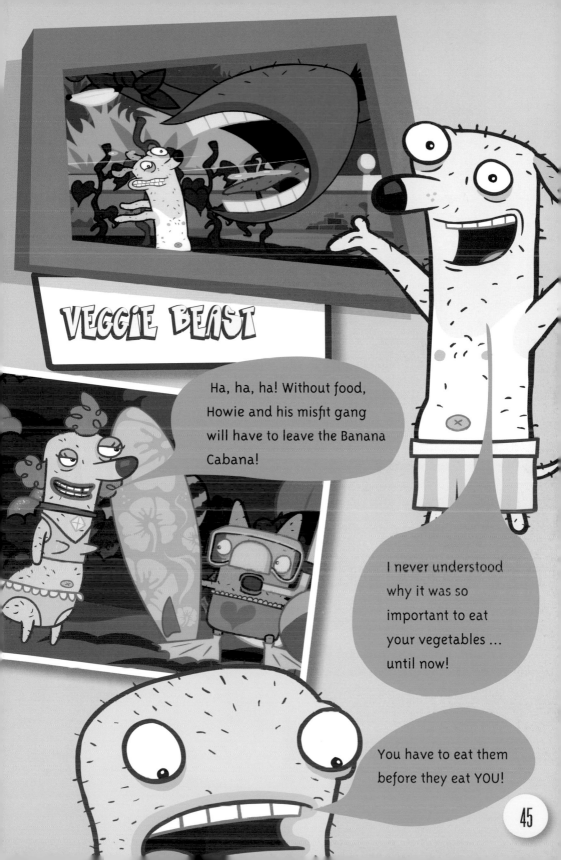

VEGGIE BEAST

Ha, ha, ha! Without food, Howie and his misfit gang will have to leave the Banana Cabana!

I never understood why it was so important to eat your vegetables ... until now!

You have to eat them before they eat YOU!

45

BANANA CABANA GUEST LIST

The Banana Cabana Hotel has seen some interesting and unusual guests since its grand opening. Here are some of the lucky animals that have survived the experience!

Come and meet Howie and his misfit crew, they've always got a room for you!

Monkey

Mole

Snake

Frog

Kitty

Camel

Squirrel

Moose

Squid

Unicorn

Snail

Rooster

Dugong

Hedgehog

Pigeon

Koala

Turtle

Butterfly

Bumblebee

Cow

BANANA CABANA FRIENDS

Who could resist the quirky charms of Howie and his crew? There's never a dull moment at the Banana Cabana ... just look at their friends!

CAP'N FIZZY

Arrrr! Fizz ahoy, me mateys!

The sparkling Cap'n is the spokesanimal, official mascot and owner of Howie's absolute favourite drink — Cap'n Fizzy's Fuzzy Orange Soda.

Likes: Fizzy things, fuzzy things, oranges
Dislikes: Dry land, grapes, broken telescopes

Oh heave yer anchor and watch it sink
Crack a Fizzy Fuzzy soda for a tasty drink
Ya'll're part of the Cap'n's crew
So guzzle with yer muzzle some orange brew. Arrr!

Did you know there's a LOT of sugar in this stuff?

MEET COCKROACH

Cockroach is best known for two things — breakdancing and having stuff fall on him. He is an expert at both! Perhaps he should become Dirk Danger's stunt double?

Likes: Breakdancing, beatboxing, chocolate milk

Dislikes: Heavy objects, slow jams, the open seas

MEET BADGER

Badger could sell fizzy drinks to Cap'n Fizzy! You name it, he sells it — and with pizzazz. When he's around, you'll end up buying things you never knew you wanted — he's a salesanimal extraordinaire!

Likes: Comfortable mattresses, high fashion, being pushy

Dislikes: Boring toilets, angry mobs, pumpkins

MEET RADIATION ROOSTER

So have you ever thought of owning your own microwave?

Radiation Rooster stands by his products ...

Aahhh, not again!

Dry mouth, flaking green skin, body parts dropping off ... (no, we're not talking about Howie after one of his famous stunts!) you've obviously been exposed to Radiation Rooster.

Need a used microwave? Radiation Rooster is your guy (if you fancy looking like an over-cooked cabbage). This fella currently holds the Banana Cabana record for having his beak fall off more times than any other rooster!

Likes: Microwaves, adventure camping, popcorn
Dislikes: Mobile phones, singing, bathrobes

I THOUGHT THAT MIGHT HAPPEN!

I do not feel well. I think I am going to be sick!

57

DIRK DANGER FAN CLUB

Welcome to the fan club of the world No.1 stunt star ... DIRK DANGER!

Name: Dirk Danger
Job: Stunting action star
Country
of origin: Swed-o-vlakia
Likes: Stunting, polka music,
             apple strudel
Dislikes: Romantic comedies,
             shopping, cold noodles

Dirk may be small, but he has a giant personality with superstar qualities. This stunt action hero is fearless — probably because he's oblivious to pain, a handy quality for a stunt animal! He never gets down in the dumps, no matter how disastrous a stunt may turn out. Always enthusiastic and with a ready smile on his face, Dirk is, nonetheless, incredibly superstitious. He will not perform a stunt unless his favourite polka music is blasting in the background!

SHRIMP

Name: Shrimp
Job: Leader of the Dirk Danger Fan Club
Likes: Following the rules, sparkles, mini golf
Dislikes: Sneezing, inane questions, being late

Best moment: Conversation with Howie that went something like this: 'Howie, you've broken "Dirk Danger Fandom Rule Number 86.576"! You're out of the Dirk Danger Fan Club!'

Worst moment: Conversation with Howie, about an hour later, that went something like this: 'Howie, I just wanted to officially apologise ... and, um, I want to welcome you back to the Dirk Danger Fan Club.'

Shrimp is a very strict (some might say killjoy!) crustacean, and he takes his job as leader of the Dirk Danger Fan Club extremely seriously. Beware: if you ever decide to break the rules, you will be crossed off Shrimp's members' list quicker than you can say 'rhinestone underpants'! Speaking of which, it is rather surprising for someone with no sense of humour at all to be seen out in *those* underpants. Yes, rhinestone underpants are Shrimp's guilty pleasure! Maybe there's hope for him yet?

Anyway, enough of the pants, back to Shrimp ... he handles all Dirk Danger's special appearances, as well as running the fan club, and it is rumoured that he even does Dirk's laundry — let's hope Dirk doesn't sweat too much with all that stunt action!

TO STUNT...

Clap your paws together and make some noise for the world's number one stunt action hero ... heeeere's DIRK DANGER!

'Good day to you, my fans of danger! Prepare to have big eyes watching me schtunting! As I sail through the hot fire pit of fire flame! Over the fallen tree of many scary teeth! And through something that could only come from a sick and twisted mind! Ready ... set ... SCHTUNT!

'Ahhhh ... whoaaa, ha, ha, whoa ... whoopsies, uh-oh, ha, ha, oof!'

...OR NOT TO STUNT!

As the familiar polka music scratches to an abrupt halt, and the sad-looking creature yodelling in beautiful Swed-o-vlakian tones stumbles over his own words, Dirk Danger fans everywhere are in shock (especially his number one fan, Howie) ...

Tragically, the famous and handsome Dirk Danger has hung up his helmet for good. Dirk realizes he has tried every stunt there is to try.

What? NO! You can't quit, you're the best schtunter, I mean stunter, of all time.

Fear not, Dirk Danger fans. If anyone can unblock his schtunter's block, it is his biggest fan, Howie ...

... and a short time later, Howie's persistence and downright annoyingness has paid off!

I am BAAAAAAACK! Howie, I want to be thanking you for unblocking my schtunting!

BEST FRIENDS

I've got a bad feeling about this.

What could possibly go wrong?

They say opposites attract, and in the case of Howie and Octo it's true — they are BFFs. Howie loves stunts, danger and doing dog things, and Octo, well … Octo doesn't like any of those things!

The two pals share a room at the Banana Cabana and are always there for each other. True, Howie is oblivious to Octo's fears (of almost everything!), and Octo is a nervous wreck most of the time he is with Howie, especially when he gets roped into Howie's crazy plans and dare-devil stunts. You might wonder why they are friends, when they have so little in common? But friendship works in strange ways, and they certainly make a strange pair …

I have an idea …

Oh no! You have another crazy, not very well-thought-out plan, don't you?

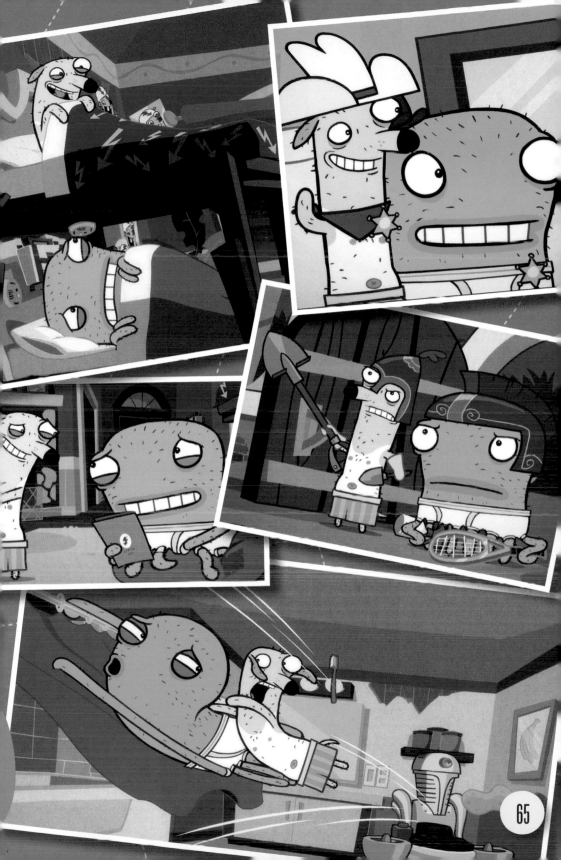

SIBLING RIVALRY

Howie is pretty sure that his sister is a delightful pink poodle who loves him very much …

Poodle is pretty sure that her brother is a goofball, and she wonders how she can possibly be related to him, as they have nothing in common.

So, sis, how would you feel about doing some Dog Stuff together?

WE CAN'T POSSIBLY BE RELATED. CAN WE?

67

alternate
THE ∧UNIVERSE
ACCORDING TO DUCK

I used to be somebody. Maybe you knew him? Tall guy with glasses?

I do not know if I can do weird.

Vegetables help me grow.

Today is the future? Wow, I can finally use my hoverboard.

At midnight I will turn into a pumpkin.

If you are getting me something, just make sure it makes me a chick magnet!

I saw the whole thing ... what happened? When?

Okie donkey!

I am going to my shed.

Aliens are taking my brain. Hee, hee. Take it away!

Raining pasta makes bananas all smushy.

I will never forget about this ... I already forgot!

Oh, you are a very good kisser for a broccoli.

I am in my happy place.

HOWIEWE'EN

AHHHHH!

Named after Howie, 'cos he invented it! Howie and the gang celebrate this scary custom every year, wearing the same costumes (well, why waste valuable fun time making new ones?), and every year Octo hides under his bed ...

I don't like being scared!

But this year, Howie persuaded Octo to try and be scary instead of being scared.

HOWIEDAYS

Happy Howiedays! My favouritest time of the year!

This one's named after Howie too, 'cos ... you guessed it ... he invented it too! Every year Howie and the gang celebrate by taking all their different traditions and combining them into the biggest and bestest holiday ever. And every year Howie tries to get Poodle and Batty to celebrate with them ...

Ha, ha, ha! The Howiedays aren't so bad once you get rid of the Howie part!

Howie's Howieday pants.

Piggy and his festive
feasty jelly.

Bunny telling the story of
Howiedays ... using puppets.

Howie's old souped-up
parade float.

Narwhal in festive flow!

Poodle can't stand it ...

73

A DAY IN THE LIFE OF PIGGY

While all the other animals in the Banana Cabana were still snoozing in bed, Piggy was already busy in the kitchen, wielding his scoop.

'Beat bananas! Chop tomatoes! Toast toast!' Piggy shouted.

Making breakfast was a whirlwind, as Piggy flew at his ingredients with all his Ninjitsu power.

'Lazy things!' Piggy yelled, when it was ready. 'Is breakfast time — *NOW!* Ninjitsu Chef Surprise! Like food — OR ELSE!'

From then on, it was work, work, work for Piggy in the kitchen all day. With just a few interruptions to dance around in his glittery pants.

Something you didn't know about Piggy: Not many animals have ever seen Piggy dance. But when they do, they admit that he's pretty light on his hooves.

At lunch he made Piggy Soup Surprise. At teatime he made doughnuts, using his excellent Doughnut Making Machine, otherwise known as Narwhal.

As Piggy placed each ball of dough on Narwhal's horn, he sang a song in his deep, gravelly voice:

'You roll the dough, you put the dough on the horn, the holey, holey, horn.'

Narwhal lay on the kitchen floor in front of Piggy, his head in his fins.

'You couldn't make cupcakes once in a while?' Narwhal asked, with a sigh. But everyone agreed that the doughnuts were necessary bundles of sugary deliciousness, and the afternoon wouldn't be the same without them.

By dinnertime, Piggy was hard at work on another of his favourite dishes: a huge pot of KABOOM Chili.

He proudly served it up in the dining room to two ginormous bulls.

'Say, how many bean types you say you got in there, Piggy Wiggy?' asked one of the bulls.

'Piggy — no Wiggy!' Piggy barked back. 'Is spicy twelve-bean type chili! Make stinky bottom go BOOM!'

The first bull tasted it.

'Eurgh — sissy water!' said the bull, spitting it back into the pot. 'You call *that* chili? I want it the way mamma used to make it.'

'So spicy, it would burn holes in your undee-pants,' the other bull joined in.

'I give YOU spicy underpants,' growled Piggy under his breath, as he stomped back into the kitchen. 'Bulls want spicy underpants, bulls get spicy underpants!'

Moments later, Piggy strode back into the dining room, with a welder's helmet on his head, carrying a jar full of seething, super-exploding KABOOM sauce. Just one drop would give the chili an almost illegal level of spicy power.

So Piggy poured exactly one drop into the pot of chili.

'What you pourin' for?' said the bull. 'Put the whole dang doodly thing in there!'

'Jar's the best part!' his friend joined in.

So Piggy dropped the jar into the pot.

PE000UW!

The chili boiled and bubbled and sent crackling orange flames into the air.

'Yee-haa!' shouted the bulls, and they gulped down the entire pot, including the jar (which had a nice crunch to it).

Then, oddly, nothing happened.

'No one ever eat Piggy Kaboom Chili and not KABOOM!' whispered Piggy to himself.

But Piggy had spoken too soon. A second later, some extremely loud alarm bells went off in the region of the bulls' underpants.

Then one of the bulls belched.

'Whooah Nelly!' he said. 'I reckon this calls for a hoe-down!'
In another moment, they were singing, dancing and tooting, and boy were they stinky.

'Too much Kaboom!' said Piggy, choking, as KABOOM clouds filled the air. With watering eyes, he just about made his way back to the kitchen. And then realised he'd have to make even more dinner for everyone else.
'Piggy never give up!'
So he picked up his knives, and went flying at whole new batch of ingredients with a Ninjitsu kick.
'Yargh!' he yelled. 'Chop suey!'

PANTS!

You will never see a finer array of underwear than that worn by Howie and friends, and the guests at the Banana Cabana. Check out this awesome display of stylish undergarments. It's pants! Which are your favourite pair?

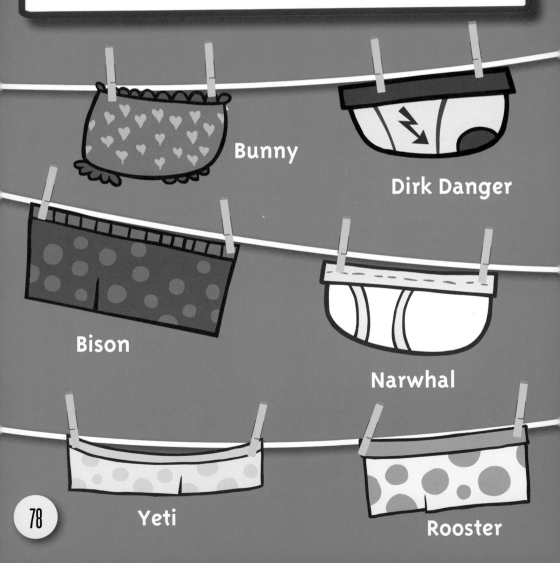

Bunny

Dirk Danger

Bison

Narwhal

Yeti

Rooster

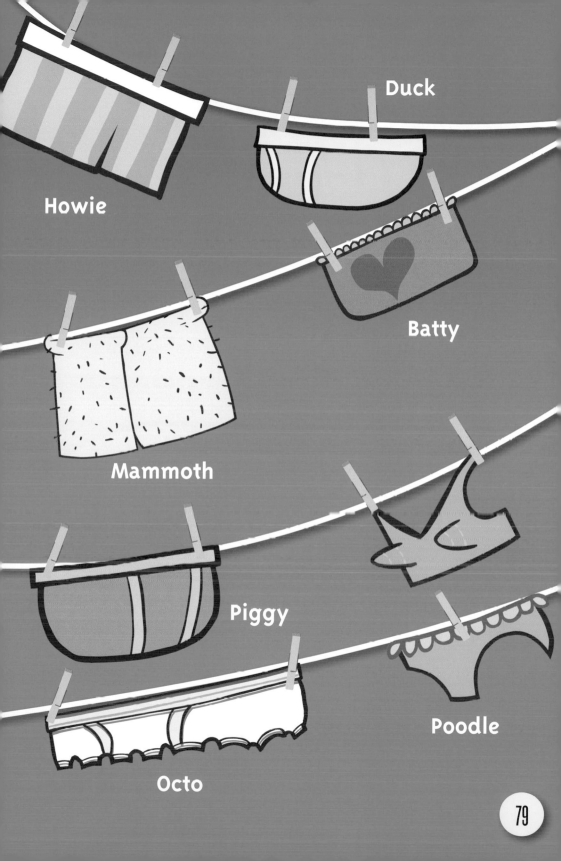

Duck

Howie

Batty

Mammoth

Piggy

Octo

Poodle

BANANA CABANA SPEAK!

Duck probably tops the bill (sorry, no pun intended!) when it comes to the strange things he says. But the rest of the gang have had their moments, that's for sure. Find a comfy chair to sit on (so you don't fall over from laughing!) and take a look at the classic one-liners on the following pages.

Have a go at making up a saying of your own for each of the gang!

_____

_____

_____

What could possibly go wrong?
Brag away. I do it all the time!
That was amazing!
Don't worry gang, I have a plan!
I'm all about sweet ideas. That's why I'm manager of this semi-fine hotel.

_____

_____

I'll go get my first aid kit.
Eight tentacles, but only two eyes. Why?
Arrrgh! Tentacle cramp! Tentacle cramp!
Paper cut! Paper cut! Oh my pupil!
Never fear! ÜBER-PUS is here!

I scoop you!
Dog thing make bad idea with head.
I give you spicy underpants!
I scoop the badness!
Piggy must remember use inside-head sneaky voice.

This can't possibly end well.
We all accomplished something unnecessary.
OK, so maybe I have a teensy-weensy bit of a temper.
Well, this day just keeps getting better and better!
I don't have a temper! I'm just ... intense.

Keep it buttery, baby!
Slip me some fin!
I got gooey glands. Spit to spare!
How can I not have a hit ring
tone yet ...?
Does this tusk make me look husky?
She'll be putty in my fins when she
gets a dose of this poetry.

_____

_____

Seriously, would it hurt someone to
give me a push?
Another sweet idea, Howie!
I loved it too, Howie! I could watch
you do that or something equally
purposeless all day!
Oh, Howie, I feel so safe doing stunts
with you!
Isn't endurance a stunt? Does
hanging upside down for twenty-
four straight hours count?

_____

_____

Remind me to fire you when this is all over!

Mwah ha ha!

You know how I despise the ill, injured or infirm! Such complainers!

It sounds like someone else has an evil minion. Only I should have an evil minion!

I don't get hung up on! I do the hanging up!

Oh, Poodle is going to be furious!

I have a long list of evil minion stuff to do!

Poodle's not gonna be happy about this!

THE SPEND A DAY WITH NARWHAL CONTEST

A Day with Narwhal, Narwhal thought, *that's one pretty special day.* And then he had a brainwave. He decided to hold a contest, to allow one of his fans to spend *a whole day* with him. They could watch him sing, and gargle. They could appreciate his blubbery beauty, close up!

If they were really lucky, they might even get a performance of his (tragically cancelled) one-whale show: *Narwhal, Oh, Narwhal, The Mighty Tusk Exposed.*

It was pretty exciting. Especially for Narwhal's number one fan, Monkey, who entered the contest a couple of times.

And then a couple more times.

And then a few more times.

And just a few more times after that.

When Monkey had entered 70,856 times, she was feeling pretty confident. Up on stage, Narwhal pulled out a ticket:

'And the winner of the Spend A Day With Narwhal Contest is … Monkey!'

Monkey could hardly believe it. She skipped! She ran up to the stage and gave Narwhal a huge hug! She took her inhaler three times!

Early the next morning, Monkey was at the Banana Cabana, watching in awe as Narwhal began his day by calling a radio station.

'Er ... hi,' Narwhal said, in a strangely un-Narwhal-like voice. 'I would like to request a song by the über-fantabulous Narwhal. Wait. What do you mean you don't have any records by Narwhal? Well ... he's fantabulous! Wait? What?!'

'Huh,' said Narwhal, putting down the phone. 'Who says I'm not a rap artist?'

Monkey found this perplexing. But Narwhal was soon busy with his next task: texting his horn polish supplier, but ignoring Monkey. Then he thought up some amazing new lyrics ...

'You've never had a real shower if you've not showered in mayo ...'

... and ignored Monkey some more.

Then he texted some record producers. Soon, even his number one fan was pretty bored. And the next time Narwhal looked up, Monkey was gone.

'Whoah,' said Narwhal. 'Where's ... what's her name?'

'Oh, she left,' said Bunny, who was sitting in the lobby.

Well, thought Narwhal. *I don't need a number one fan! I'll be fine without her.* His stomach lurched. Suddenly the room seemed very empty. *Without a number one fan,* he thought, *I'll just be ... average!*

AVERAGE! It was all too much. Narwhal keeled over. He lay on the ground and began to cry. And he was still weeping gently to himself when a crowd of giggling, yelping animals burst through the door and stampeded into the room.

'Oh … look,' said Narwhal sadly, 'It's my number 2 through 37 fans.'

'Is it true?' asked a beaming turtle.

'Is what true?' said Narwhal.

'You've lost your number one fan? It's all over the internets!'

'It's true,' Narwhal sighed. 'And I'll understand if none of you want to be my fan either …'

'But we ALL want to be your number one fan!' they shouted.

'Oh. OH!' Narwhal sprang to his feet. 'Well, baby, of course you do! Form a line, ladies, the competition is about to begin. Easy, easy, don't barge, you ladies know I'm ticklish!'

And very soon, Turtle was Narwhal's new number one fan. And Narwhal was crooning his heart out on stage in the lounge, in front of a whole crowd of adoring admirers.

'Whop dop deedle deedly dee, they put cheese all over me!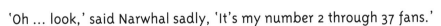

Well, I danced with them and they danced with me, cheese on my knees!'
he sang.

Ah, there it is, thought Narwhal. *The soothing sound of applause.*

He sang some more of his latest hits, including 'What Does It Mean When It
Smells Like That?' and 'Don't Shave A Banana With Your Eyes!'

By the end of the set, his horn was tingling with happiness.

'Thank you and goodnight!' he shouted, as his fans whooped
some more.

That night, when Narwhal was
tucked up in bed, he thought about
how lucky he was. He got to spend
the day with Narwhal *every* day.

CABANA COLOURING

Grab your pens and pencils and give Howie and the gang a colour makeover. If you don't want to get on the wrong side of Poodle (and we strongly advise that you don't!) then you'd better stick to pink for her.

DUCK'S D.I.Y. GALLERY

'I am going to my shed ... I can fix this!'

Take a peek at some of Duck's finest moments of inspiration!

I turned the toilets into mini volcanoes!

Behold ... the Super-Duper-Pig-Stretcher!

Wheeeeee!

I booby-trapped the sun!

Let's get fun-kay!

A giant can needs a ... giant can-opener!

The booger chair! Yes, I made it.

This will really blow you away.

91

DUCK'S QUIZ

Now that you have nearly finished reading this book, I am going to give you a test to see if you have been paying attention. You can thank me if you like. If you would like to thank me in the form of a gift, please do not get me a booger chair. I already have one of those.

So, how well do you know me? Take the test and enjoy. And do not forget the onions. Or do I mean tomatoes?

I. What is my full name?

2. I am the king of my own country. What is it called?

3. Where do I have some of my best ideas?

4. Where do I sleep?

5. What is my favourite flavour?

6. Howie once wanted to make me his hero. What did I think he meant?

7. What makes happy endings?

8. What did I once say to a broccoli?

9. What is better to eat than to wear?

10. Raining pasta makes what all smushy?

Turn to page 106 for answers.

BUNNY'S BIG BANANA CABANA ACTIVITY PACK

What are Howie and the gang up to in this picture? Study the scene and see if you can spot all the things shown on the right.

Why not have a go at these fun puzzle activities while you relax by the Cabana's pool, enjoying a tasty snack from Piggy's kitchen, before joining in with one of my fabulous swimming exercise classes ... come on then, get on with it, I haven't got all day!

Turn to page 106 for answers.

SPOT-THE-DIFFERENCE

Howie shares a room at the Banana Cabana with his best friend, Octo. Poor ol' Octo doesn't always get a good night's sleep though, 'cos Howie is always talking about dangerous stunts ... which makes Octo quiver and shiver in his bed. Can you spot the eleven differences between these two pictures? How many smoke detectors can you find in total — like this one: Octo might need to test them all before he can go to sleep!

Turn to page 107 for answers.

WHO'S WHO?

Oh, no! Howie has accidentally broken all the light bulbs in the Banana Cabana while trying out a new stunt, and everything has been plunged into darkness. When Duck eventually fixes the lights, everything is in chaos and there are guests wandering all over the place.

Can you work out who the guests are, so that you can help them back to their rooms?

Turn to page 107 for answers.

CABANA WORDSEARCH

Howie loves a challenge, especially if it involves danger and stunts! But when it comes to wordsearches, he just doesn't seem to be able to get his head around them. Quick, give Howie a paw finding all the words listed below … before he starts chasing his tail instead.

Words to find:

FIRST AID KIT	YETI	STUNTS	NINJITSU
CAP'N FIZZY	SHRIMP	RADIATION	ROOSTER
POLKA	HOWIEWE'EN	HOWIEDAYS	PANTS
BANANA	SCOOP	DOG THING	

```
M D R C G F S H R I M P Y U H Y I N B U
T R I A C A P N F I Z Z Y U O O J W B L
H T G P D O L D L N Y K W D W H X N P R
M V V I Y I R U H B L W O V I D B R O Y
T H U E K M A Z M O A T F A E J K Z E E
O N M X W H F T F K W B P Y W L R T J T
D H E A T Z Q I G Q I P A E O K Y N I
M Z T S W G W E X O V L E B E K I F C R
A C B C H H H Y J B N J P D N N P I V W
S C O O P C W C D G E F O K A I H R E O
M O K Q O U J F F O N Q L Q S Y Q S N X
I C K A C O T R Z S G U K O H G S T V R
B I Y A I M C F I S P T A Y H T Q A V R
X C F W X R O O S T E R H A L T W I M P
T B A N A N A N H K S K C I M L W D Q A
M E V T J O L X W M E O O H N F R K T N
B S E R L A I L B T Y V I I Q G F I V T
G P U S A V A T U F L F H U V E G T A S
I X S T U N T S T M V M B D Z I N I J C
J M C K O N I N J I T S U K K J F J V U
```

Turn to page 107 for answers.

PIGGY'S SPICY SUDOKU

Remember, each of the six objects must only appear once on each horizontal and vertical line.

Piggy is not a happy chef. Someone has been in his kitchen and messed things up. Finish this tricky Sudoku puzzle by filling in the blank squares with the correct food or utensil from Piggy's kitchen. Help him tidy up before he has to scoop someone!

Turn to page 108 for answers.

BUNNY'S BIG BANANA CROSSWORD

You must be an Almost Naked Animals expert by now, having read this book cover to cover! So are you up for the final challenge? Work out the clues to all the questions below and fill in this big crossword. If you get it all correct, Howie just might make you employee of the month, for life!

Across

1) He loves following the rules and he is the leader of the Dirk Danger Fan Club. Who is he? (6)

3) Who would rather sandpaper their own eyes than do dog stuff with Howie? (6)

4) This little fella can really dance — when he's not being squashed by falling objects! (9)

8) Who is the greatest Ninjitsu Chef of all time? (6,6)

9) Likes princesses, dislikes armpits (who doesn't?). (5)

Down

2) Who sells used microwaves and holds a record for his beak falling off more than anyone else's? (9,7)

3) What kind of music does Dirk Danger have to have playing when he does a stunt? (5,5)

5) Who is the mascot for the gang's absolute favourite fuzzy orange drink? (4,5)

6) What is the name of the actor who pretends to be Howie's long-lost brother? (5)

7) He's big, and he is the fiercest competitive watermelon eater the gang has ever seen. (4)

Turn to page 109 for answers.

EMPLOYEE OF THE MONTH

Have you enjoyed your stay? We hope you've had lots of fun! By now you should've got a pretty (or ugly!) good idea of what we're all like.

We welcome feedback (OK, we probably won't be too happy if it's not good …!) — it helps us make your stay even more enjoyable. Please fill in the following with your comments (nice comments get a free weekend break at the Banana Cabana) and give us all your star rating.

HOWIE

Skills: _____

Needs to improve on: _____

Star rating: _____

Howie deserves … stars because:

_____

_____

OCTO

Skills: _____

Needs to improve on: _____

Star rating: _____

Octo deserves … stars because:

_____

_____

BUNNY

Skills: _____

Needs to improve on: _____

Star rating: _____

Bunny deserves ... stars because:

_____

_____

PIGGY

Skills: _____

Needs to improve on: _____

Star rating: _____

Piggy deserves ... stars because:

_____

_____

DUCK

Skills: _____

Needs to improve on: _____

Star rating: _____

Duck deserves ... stars because:

_____

_____

NARWAL

Skills: _____

Needs to improve on: _____

Star rating: _____

Narwal deserves ... stars because:

_____

_____

SLOTH

Skills: _____

Needs to improve on: _____

Star rating: _____

Sloth deserves ... stars because:

_____

_____

POODLE

Skills: _____

Needs to improve on: _____

Star rating: _____

Poodle deserves ... stars because:

_____

_____

BATTY

Skills: _____

Needs to improve on: _____

Star rating: _____

Batty deserves ... stars because:

_____

_____

ANSWERS

Pages 92-93 Duck's Quiz

1. My full name is Archibald William Nightingale Duck III.

2. Shedsylvania

3. I have some of my best ideas in my shed.

4. I sleep in the Banana Cabana's store cupboard.

5. Green. Particularly green crayons.

6. I thought Howie wanted to make me a delicious hero sandwich! Hee, hee, hee. It tickles when he bites.

7. Bouncy landings make a happy endings.

8. 'Oh, you are a very good kisser for a broccoli.'

9. It is better to eat dessert than to wear it.

10. Raining pasta makes bananas all smushy.

Pages 94-95 Search and Find

Page 96 Spot the difference

There are five smoke alarms in total between the two pictures.

Page 97 Who's who?

a = Duck

b = Cockroach

c = Radiation Rooster

d = Dirk Danger

e = Yeti

f = Shrimp

g = Monkey

h = Cap'n Fizzy

Page 98 Wordsearch

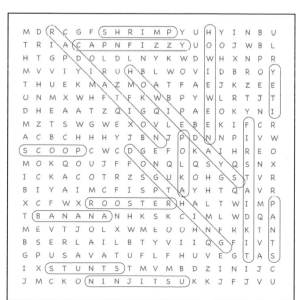

Page 99 Sudoku

1 =   2 =   3 =   4 =   5 =   6 =

Page 100-101 Bunny's Big Banana Crossword

	1S	H	2R	I	M	P

Across and Down:

1. SHRIMP
2. RADIATION
3. POODLE
4. COCKROACH
5. CAPNFIZZ
6. LARRY
7. YETI
8. MASTERFERRET
9. BUNNY

POOLCAMUSIC
POONRSTR
MASTERFERRET
BUNNY

Iye, Iye, Iye!
A big Banana Cabana goodbye!

Hope you enjoyed your stay. Come and visit us soon ... what could possibly go wrong?